Sammy S

Superm

Moira Andrew

Sammy Snake had a splendid idea.
"Letterland needs a supermarket,"
he thought. "I will open one.
It will sell all sorts of
scrumptious things!"

This book belongs to

....

....

Useful words

(in the order they appear in this book)

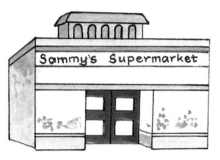

supermarket

trolleys

shelves

till

freezer

fruit

money

cake counter

dandelions

doughnuts

mangoes

mushrooms

mustard

baked beans

cabbage

Grey letters represent silent letters.

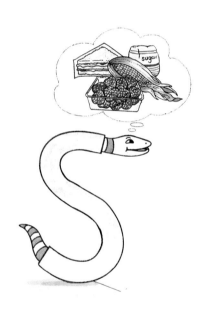

Sammy started to make a list of things he needed.

"I'll need trolleys, lots of shelves and some tills," he said to himself.

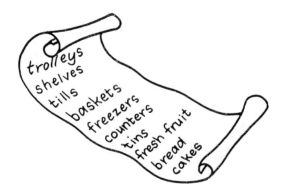

trolleys
shelves
tills
baskets
freezers
counters
tins
fresh fruit
bread
cakes

trolleys
shelves
tills
baskets
freezers
counters
tins
freshfruit
bread
cakes
sandwiches
vegetables
boxes

Sammy asked some of the Letterlanders to help him.

"I'd be happy to help," said Hairy Hat Man. He worked very hard carrying lots of heavy boxes.

Fireman Fred came along too, and finished filling the shelves. Then he filled the freezers and put out some fresh fruit.

Ticking Tess said she would take the money at the till. Clever Cat wanted to serve on the cake counter.

On Saturday, the supermarket shelves were stacked and everything was ready. The sun shone and Sammy Snake went to open the doors.

Dippy Duck dashed in to find something delicious for dinner. "Do you sell dandelions?" she said.

"Sorry," said Sammy.

"Then I'll have doughnuts instead," said Dippy.

"Mangoes, mushrooms, mustard ...," muttered Munching Mike.

"Mmm ..., they will be marvellous with some metal," he said moving along the shelves.

Bouncy Ben came in to buy some baked beans. He tried to take a tin from a big pile. Bang! Bounce! All the baked bean tins came tumbling down.

Fireman Fred and Sammy Snake
came over to help.

"I'm sorry," sniffed Ben.

"Don't fuss," said Fred putting
two tins into Ben's basket.

Clever Cat came out from behind the cake counter. She put carrots, crisps and a cabbage into her trolley. Then she went to talk to Ticking Tess at the till.

"Time to close," said Sammy Snake. "The supermarket has had a simply splendid start," he said as he slithered along.

"Thank you everyone." And a

sleepy Sammy slid off home to bed.

The Letterlanders

 Annie Apple

 Bouncy Ben

 Clever Cat

 Dippy Duck

 Eddy Elephant

 Fireman Fred

 Golden Girl

 Hairy Hat Man

 Impy Ink

 Jumping Jim

 Kicking King

 Lucy Lamp Lady

 Munching Mike

 Naughty Nick

 Oscar Orange

 Poor Peter

 Quarrelsome Queen

 Robber Red

 Sammy Snake

 Ticking Tess

 Uppy Umbrella

 Vase of Violets

 Wicked Water Witch

 Max and Maxine

 Yellow Yo-yo Man

 Zig Zag Zebra

This edition produced for
The Book People Ltd., Hall Wood Avenue,
Haydock, St. Helens WA11 9UL

Published by Collins Educational
An imprint of HarperCollins*Publishers* Ltd
77-85 Fulham Palace Road
London W6 8JB

© Lyn Wendon 1998

First published 1998
Reprinted 1998

ISBN 0 00 303405 4

British Library Cataloguing in Publication Data
A catalogue record for this book is available from the British Library.

Written by Moira Andrew
Illustrated by Maggie Downer
Designed by Michael Sturley and Sally Boothroyd
Consultant: Lyn Wendon, originator of Letterland

Printed by Printing Express, Hong Kong